OCR AS Critical Thinking

Unit 2: Assessing & Developing Argument

Jill Swale

Philip Allan Updates, an imprint of Hodder Education, an Hachette UK company, Market Place, Deddington, Oxfordshire OX15 0SE

Orders
Bookpoint Ltd, 130 Milton Park, Abingdon, Oxfordshire OX14 4SB

tel: 01235 827827, fax: 01235 400401

e-mail: education@bookpoint.co.uk

Lines are open 9.00 a.m.–5.00 p.m., Monday to Saturday, with a 24-hour message answering service. You can also order through the Philip Allan Updates website: www.philipallan.co.uk

ISBN 978-0-340-97381-3

First printed 2008

Impression number 6

Year 2013 2012 2011

Printed in Spain

Hachette UK's policy is to use papers that are natural, renewable and recyclable products and made from wood grown in sustainable forests. The logging and manufacturing processes are expected to conform to the environmental regulations of the country of origin.

Introduction

This is the second of two workbooks designed to support and complement AS courses in Critical Thinking for the OCR 2008 specification. It will help you practise the skills required in Unit 2 and provide you with essential information and useful examples.

Section 1: Analysis of argument

The exercise at the beginning of this section should remind you of the components of arguments studied in Unit 1, before introducing some of the flaws in reasoning to be discussed later in the workbook. The section then goes on to extend your ability to recognise these components, since one of the skills tested in critical thinking is the ability to analyse reasoning (Assessment Objective 1). The content moves from familiar to less familiar elements of argument, so it is advisable to tackle the exercises in order.

Section 2: Evaluating arguments

This section teaches you to identify strengths and weaknesses in reasoning, building on skills gained in Unit 1 in evaluating reasoning (Assessment Objective 2). You will learn the names of well-known flaws and appeals and should be able to explain how you have identified these features in a particular context and why they constitute poor reasoning.

Section 3: Multiple-choice questions

This section provides tips and practice in answering multiple-choice questions, which test your ability to analyse arguments, evaluate evidence and identify flaws in reasoning.

Section 4: Developing reasoned arguments

This section teaches you to develop and write well-structured and convincing arguments, and to suggest additional material that might support or challenge existing arguments; these skills are tested by Assessment Objective 3.

Section 5: Specimen examination paper

Once you have practised each skill, the workbook provides a full-length practice paper for this unit, modelled on the 2008 specimen paper supplied by OCR. **Be aware that real examination papers vary from year to year and can differ considerably from the specimen**, so practise as many as you can. Try to complete the paper in 1 hour 30 minutes, the time allocated to the real exam.

After completing this workbook, you should continue to practise your skills by applying them to real-life situations such as news reports, discussions in the media and debates in the classroom. Remember that the essential purpose of critical thinking is to make you more aware of the need to reason carefully about issues that concern you in your everyday life.

We hope this workbook will help you in your studies and in your examination.

Getting started

In Unit 2, you will gain a deeper understanding of how to analyse arguments and recognise their strengths and weaknesses, as well as learning the skills necessary to write well-organised arguments of your own. The activity below should remind you of some of the components of arguments studied in Unit 1 and give you a foretaste of new topics covered in Unit 2.

Exercise 1

Read the passage **Prison officers' right to strike** and answer the questions in the spaces provided.

Prison officers' right to strike

1 Justice Secretary Jack Straw has vowed to ask Parliament for extra powers to stop prison officers from going on strike or taking any other sort of industrial action if the Prison Officers' Association cannot reach a voluntary no-strike agreement with the government through current negotiations. Straw's tough threats come in response to a 12-hour strike by prison officers in August 2007, during which £220,000 of damage was done at Lancaster Farms prison, with inmates smashing plumbing systems, breaking windows and starting fires.

2 Although the government opposes the right to strike for prison officers and police, as their roles are so essential for maintaining public order, being allowed to take industrial action is a basic human right.

3 Those who work in the public services often have a strong sense of vocation, so it is tempting for the government departments employing such people to underpay them in order to keep public expenditure at a manageable level. In 2007 an independent pay review body recommended a 2.5% pay rise for prison officers, but the government staged the rise as 1.5% in April and a further 1% in November, reducing the value of the award to a below-inflation pay increase.

4 Prison officers deserve fair work conditions in exchange for the increased dangers they face on a daily basis. The dramatic rise in prisoner numbers, from 60,000 in 1997 to the present-day 80,000, has led to more offenders being crammed into the same confined space, resulting in heightened tensions. Twice as many male prison officers were attacked by inmates in 2006 as in 2000. The increase in the figure for female officers was a staggering 121%.

5 Jack Straw supported the war in Iraq, which is now widely recognised as a disaster, so it is clear that we should reject his idea that prison officers should be banned from striking. Other workers such as teachers are just as essential, as there would be chaos if schoolchildren were allowed to roam the streets all day. However, teachers are still allowed to strike for better pay and conditions, so prison officers should have the same rights.

6 Chairman of the Prison Officers' Association Colin Moses said on this matter: 'Surely we should be treated as well, if not better, than the prisoners we look after.'

7 If prison officers are not rewarded with better conditions, many will leave the service and there will be a severe shortage of people to manage the prisons. Many prisons will have to be closed down and dangerous offenders will roam the streets, making life terrifying for us all. There is a stark choice before us: to improve the working conditions of prison officers or to risk massive danger to the public.

8 Unlike the police, prison officers work behind closed doors, so until recently members of the public have been unaware of the dangers these individuals face and how poorly they are paid. Striking can be the only way to draw attention to work-related grievances if employers take no notice of complaints. Now their dire situation has become known, the public must campaign for prison officers' right to strike for better conditions.

1 Sometimes arguments are surrounded by scene setting or explanation. Identify the point at which the actual argument starts by writing down the first sentence of it.

2 Within the first sentence of the argument, some reasoning is presented that opposes the thrust of the rest of the argument. Name the component that has this function.

3 Identify the evidence in paragraph 3.

4 Identify the reason in paragraph 4.

5 Identify the conclusion of the argument.

6 Examine the argument from paragraph 5 to the end. It contains some flaws in reasoning which you will learn to recognise in Unit 2. See if you can spot them now by writing down the paragraph in which they occur and the first and last few words.

a A **slippery-slope argument**. This is an extreme type of hypothetical argument, a prediction about the future in which matters go from bad to worse, leading to disaster. Not all the links in the chain of argument are necessarily convincing.

b **Poor analogy**. A comparison is employed to support the reasoning, but the situations being compared are not similar enough to carry the argument.

c ***Ad hominem***. The argument is criticised on the grounds that the person putting it forward is not to be trusted, but the reason provided for condemning the arguer is not relevant to this topic.

d **Restricted choices**. The reader is invited to choose the least bad of two options, ignoring the fact that there might be other possibilities.

e An **appeal to pity**. There is an attempt to persuade the reader by arousing emotion rather than using reasoned argument.

7 The passage mentions the damage resulting from a 12-hour prison officers' strike at Lancaster Farms prison, caused by prisoners locked in their cells without supervision. Suggest two other reasons against allowing prison officers to strike.

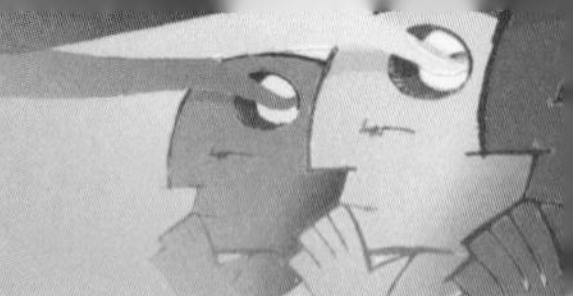

Exercise 1 has introduced the three skills required in Unit 2:

- **Assessment Objective 1:** analysing reasoning by breaking it down into its component parts such as reasons, evidence, counter-arguments and conclusions. You need to be able to recognise the structure of an argument and name its parts. Many of these components were covered in Unit 1 but some will be new.
- **Assessment Objective 2:** evaluating reasoning. You need to be able to recognise strengths and weaknesses in reasoning, such as inadequate and irrelevant evidence and false assumptions, which you encountered in Unit 1. In addition, you will encounter new flaws in reasoning, such as *ad hominem* and slippery-slope arguments. You will need to explain how you are able to recognise the flaws in a particular context and why they constitute poor reasoning.
- **Assessment Objective 3:** developing your own well-structured arguments. You will learn to write an argument supporting or challenging a given conclusion, providing your own reasons and evidence and including particular components. Question 7 in Exercise 1 asked you to provide two reasons of your own against allowing prison officers to strike. In an examination question, this task could be developed, asking you to write a short, carefully structured argument against allowing prison officers to strike, including two or more reasons, supporting evidence, a counter-argument, an intermediate conclusion and a conclusion.

Section 1: Analysis of argument
Intermediate conclusions

In Unit 1, you used your skills of analysis (Assessment Objective 1) to understand the structure of simple arguments, with several reasons leading to a conclusion. However, most long arguments proceed in a series of steps.

Several reasons may lead to a preliminary conclusion partway through the argument. That conclusion may, on its own or supported by further reasons, lead on to a final conclusion. The preliminary conclusion is known as an **intermediate conclusion** (IC), and the final one is referred to as the **main** or **overall conclusion** (C).

Below is an example. Look at it carefully and identify the main conclusion. After this, try to identify all the reasons (R1, R2 etc.) and locate an intermediate conclusion partway through the argument.

Many people in Britain are unable to find suitable work for years. They frequently have no savings to fall back on. We are a humane society and do not wish people to starve, so it is right that we make welfare benefits available to them. However, taxpayers often protest at this expense and worry that those receiving unemployment benefits may have little incentive to seek work. The Conservatives' idea — that those who refuse three reasonable job offers should be made to do community work in exchange for their benefits — is therefore sound.

This is how it works:

Many people in Britain are unable to find suitable work for years. (R1)

They frequently have no savings to fall back on. (R2)

We are a humane society and do not wish people to starve, (R3)

so it is right that we make welfare benefits available to them. (IC)

However, taxpayers often protest at this expense (R4)

and worry that those receiving unemployment benefits may have little incentive to seek work. (R5)

The Conservatives' idea — that those who refuse three reasonable job offers should be made to do community work in exchange for their benefits — is therefore sound. (C)

Unfortunately, the components of an argument do not always follow in such a predictable order. You will recall that in a simple argument, a conclusion can precede the reasons that support it. Likewise, a main conclusion may precede an intermediate conclusion in a more complex argument. The words 'intermediate' and 'main' refer to the order in which a logical thinker would work through the reasons and draw these conclusions, not necessarily the order in which they are presented on the page.

Many writers present their overall conclusion first for dramatic effect. They may also make use of more than one intermediate conclusion. Look carefully at the argument on p. 8, in which the main conclusion from the previous argument has been moved to the beginning and a second intermediate conclusion has been added.

The Conservatives' idea — that those who refuse three reasonable job offers should be made to do community work in exchange for their benefits — is to be welcomed. (C)

Many people in Britain are unable to find suitable work for years. (R1)

They frequently have no savings to fall back on. (R2)

We are a humane society and do not wish people to starve, (R3)

so it is right that we make welfare benefits available to them. (IC1)

However, taxpayers often protest at this expense (R4)

and worry that those receiving unemployment benefits may have little incentive to seek work. (R5)

It is therefore necessary to think of some humane way to encourage the long-term unemployed back to work. (IC2)

Exercise 2

Identify all the reasons, intermediate conclusions and main conclusions in the following arguments by writing the parts out in a similar way to the models above. Look for reason indicator words such as *because* and *as*, and conclusion indicator words such as *so* and *therefore* as clues. When there are no indicator words, you can still try out the two different types of testing words, such as *because* and *so*, to see which fits best.

1 There should be stiff penalties for able-bodied people who park in spaces marked for the disabled. Those whose mobility is limited need to be able to park as close as possible to shops and libraries. Some need the extra-wide spaces to be able to manoeuvre their wheelchairs. It is therefore quite unreasonable for fit people to occupy these parking spaces.

2 Some of the incapacity benefit paid to about a million people could be saved with greater effort from the government. There are currently 2.6 million people, apparently too sick or disabled to work, receiving incapacity benefit. Many of these may once have been unfit for work but have now recovered. The government should organise health assessments to check the legitimacy of people's claims. There are also genuinely disabled people who would prefer to work if offered suitable jobs. There is a need to adapt work premises and processes to meet the needs of the disabled.

Analogies

An **analogy** is a suggestion that two situations are sufficiently similar to make parallels between them. The arguer maintains that what is true for one must be true for the other. This device is often used to take us from a familiar or emotive situation about which we have some certainty to a less familiar situation, in the hope that we will draw similar conclusions. For example:

Most of us could not bring ourselves to kill an animal, so it cannot be right to buy the meat of animals that other people have killed on our behalf.

If there are more relevant similarities than differences between the situations, an analogy may lend strength to an argument. However, an analogy can never prove an argument with absolute certainty, as the two situations are not exactly the same.

If there are significant differences between the two situations, it is known as a weak analogy or **disanalogy** and is a **flaw** in the reasoning. In the examination, you may be asked to identify analogies in a passage and to evaluate the degree to which they support the conclusion. This means stating ways in which the two situations are both similar and different and judging the degree to which this strengthens or weakens the argument.

Exercise 3

Evaluate the analogies below by stating briefly:

- the two situations that are being likened and how the analogy is intended to further the argument
- relevant similarities that make the analogy convincing
- significant differences between the situations that the writer has not acknowledged
- how these differences might weaken the analogy and the claim resting upon it
- whether there are any other problems with the analogy (for example factual inaccuracies)
- in conclusion, whether you feel the analogy is effective in strengthening the argument

1 Children are taught by their parents to treat their pets kindly and are encouraged to care for rodents such as mice and gerbils. Therefore, it cannot be right for adults to put down poison when they discover mice and rats in their houses and sheds.

2 You wouldn't expect to go into a restaurant and leave without paying, so when you come home for the university holidays it is unreasonable to expect your parents to supply you with free meals.

3 Everyone agrees that people should be encouraged to use public transport more often in order to keep global warming to a minimum. Displaying fairy lights at Christmas is inessential and a waste of energy, so there should be a government campaign to discourage this practice.

Identifying general principles

Principles are rule-like statements or guidelines for action that are intended to apply over a wide range of situations. Not everyone shares the same principles, as they are in essence statements of opinion about priorities or how one should behave. This is illustrated by the following principles, all of which are controversial:

- All workers should be paid according to their needs.
- All workers should be paid according to how necessary their job is to society.
- All workers should be paid according to how long their training is.
- All workers should be paid the same hourly rate.

In some arguments, principles are stated explicitly and function as reasons to support a particular viewpoint, whereas in others they may be implied, assumed or absent altogether. In critical thinking examinations, you may be asked to:

- **identify** the general principle being applied in an argument
- **evaluate** how consistently the principle is applied, whether it conflicts with other principles, reasons or evidence within the argument, or possibly how reasonable the principle is
- **construct** an argument on a given topic, including a principle as a reason
- **construct** an argument on a given topic, supporting or challenging a principle supplied

Exercise 4

1 Identify the general principles in the following account and write them in the space provided.

> Jasvinder Sanghera fled her Derby home at 15 to avoid a forced marriage. She has written a moving biography, *Shame*, about her own experiences and those of her five sisters, all of whom were forced into disastrous marriages, one ending in suicide. Jasvinder, a Sikh, eventually set up Karma Nirvana, a community-based project that supports South Asian women affected by domestic violence and honour-based crimes. No one should have to marry against their will.
>
> The need for projects like Jasvinder's is illustrated by the recent murder investigation concerning Shafilea Ahmed, 17, whose body was discovered in 2004. Community workers said the Muslim teenager from Warrington had approached them for a place in a refuge in order to escape from her parents who, she claimed, were forcing her into an arranged marriage and had beaten her and confiscated her savings. Support should be available to all minors, as parents do not always act in their children's best interests, even when their intentions are good. Jasvinder admits that her parents knew that arranged marriages were preferred in the local community and were doing their best for her, but nevertheless forced marriages are illegal in Britain.

2 Read the extract from a school prospectus below and answer the questions that follow.

> Willownook School is academically successful. Each year there are 10 or more Oxford or Cambridge candidates, with many obtaining places.
>
> Since September 2002, the school has been designated a Sports College by the Specialist Schools and Academies Trust. This has been a central contribution to the school's development and creativity.
>
> Out-of-classroom activities at Willownook are many and varied, as we believe in equal access to enriching experiences for all, and extracurricular activities are regarded as central to the pupils' education. Many competitions and activities are House-based, and the school enjoys a thriving life of music and drama. Sporting traditions are strong, supported by excellent facilities. When they join the school, all students are invited to attend after-school clubs in a range of sports; after 2 months, those with the greatest aptitude are selected for the school teams and continue to be offered training in the clubs. We have an exceptional range of teams and a strong fixture list.

a Identify the principle in the prospectus.

b To what extent is the content of the prospectus consistent with the principle? Explain your answer.

c What else would it be useful to know in order to be sure that the school is 'academically successful'?

Other important terms

Unit 2 requires candidates to demonstrate understanding and make accurate use of various terms relevant to critical thinking. Some of these you have encountered already in Unit 1, but others may be new.

Assumption

An assumption is an **unstated** part of an argument, something that is taken for granted and not mentioned directly because it seems obvious to the arguer. Assumptions may or may not be sound. The conclusion of the argument is based upon explicitly stated reasons and implicit assumptions.

Chloe must have been present at school today because her work appeared on my shelf mid-morning.

The assumption here is that Chloe was the person who put her work on the teacher's shelf, whereas it might have been a friend of Chloe's who left it there. In this instance, the assumption could be false.

The statement *Chloe must have been present at school today* is **not** called an assumption in critical thinking, even though in ordinary language people might say that the teacher was assuming this. Because it is **stated**, we should instead call it a **conjecture**, **belief** or **claim**.

When asked to identify assumptions in a passage, you are unlikely to score full marks if you simply write them out. It is usually necessary to clarify why the assumption may be false by pointing out alternative possibilities, perhaps using the word *whereas*. You may encounter multiple-choice questions that ask which of several points need to be assumed for a conclusion to be reached. False assumptions count as **flaws** or **weaknesses** within an argument, so you can refer to them if asked to assess the reasoning.

Implications and inferences

An implication is a point that is not stated **explicitly** in a passage but can be worked out from the evidence available. However, there is always a chance that the reader may interpret the evidence incorrectly, inferring something that is not in fact the case. People sometimes confuse implications and inferences, as the terms are often found together in the same context. Remember that a passage or speaker **implies** something, whereas the reader or listener **infers** the **implicit meaning**. Here is an example of correct usage.

*We can **infer** from the news that a pair of twins who were separated at birth and later married each other did not know their own true identities. We can also **infer** that they were not identical twins as they must have been a male and a female. The news story **implies** that this was a conventional marriage and not a civil partnership ceremony between same-sex partners.*

Sometimes you may be asked what a passage is most likely to imply and what alternative explanation could possibly be inferred.

Ambiguity

Ambiguous statements can be interpreted in different ways because of double or even multiple possible meanings. For example, if a policewoman 'booked a hairdresser' this could mean recording the hairdresser's name because she had committed an offence or arranging a hairdressing appointment. Sometimes it is not entirely clear in an argument which of several possible meanings of a key word is intended, or the meaning of the word may subtly shift during the course of the passage. Here is a well-known example of the latter.

Teacher: What are you doing, boy?
Pupil: Nothing, sir!
Teacher: Well you shouldn't be doing nothing. You should be working!

In the above example, the teacher is deliberately misunderstanding the boy's use of the word *nothing* in order to 'win the argument'.

You may encounter multiple-choice questions where you have to select from a set of options the meaning closest to the use of a word in the passage.

Other important terms

- **Assess:** evaluate arguments or parts of them by identifying their strengths and weaknesses.
- **Belief:** a principle, proposition or idea accepted as true; beliefs or opinions must be distinguished from established knowledge.
- **Challenge:** a response to an argument or assertion, suggesting it may not be true. In Unit 2, you will be asked to write your own argument either to challenge or support the main conclusion of a passage.
- **Coherent argument:** a meaningful argument, where the steps flow logically from one to another and all points are relevant.
- **Consistent argument:** an argument without internal contradictions.
- **Contradiction:** when two or more claims undermine each other, showing that at least one cannot be completely true.
- **Converse:** the converse of a statement is where the order of parts has been reversed, so the converse of *The policeman shot the woman* is *The woman shot the policeman*.
- **Counter:** a counter-argument or counter-claim opposes the main argument or claim. A counter-example undermines the main argument. *To counter* can also be used as a verb.
- **Reasoning:** a logical pattern of thought, making use of reasons, evidence, analogies and other components to persuade or to work something out.
- **Refute:** prove a claim wrong.
- **Repudiate:** emphatically reject an argument or idea, whether or not it is correct or justified.
- **Structure:** the structure of the argument refers to its various components or elements and the order in which they function to support its claims and enable the arguer to draw a conclusion.

Exercise 5

Read the following account and answer the questions that follow.

1 What can be done about juvenile crime, such as the murder of Garry Newlove, who went out to stop drunken youths from vandalising his car? Conservative leader David Cameron believes that Britain's streets have been 'lost' to thugs and that there is a need for 'big social, cultural and political change' to tackle the problem of social disorder. He has proposed a national volunteer scheme for 16-year-olds.

2 'Every 16-year-old should do this as part of growing up, part of becoming an adult,' he said. 'I'm absolutely determined to make this work. In my view, this is something so important for the future of our society...we can't afford not to make it work.'

3 Governments have a duty to provide opportunities for young people. Cameron's proposal is to encourage all 16-year-olds to spend a summer holiday undertaking a number of projects to help give them a sense of worth and a place in society. The course would include a week's residential course, 4 weeks of community service, such as working with the elderly or in a developing country, and a week's physical challenge — like Army training or mountain climbing — to take young people out of their 'comfort zone'.

4 National military service, which was abolished in Britain in 1960, made it compulsory for able-bodied males aged between 17 and 21 to spend 18 months serving with one of the armed forces. Such an activity, according to Cameron, 'prepares teenagers for their responsibilities as adult citizens, enables them to meet people from different backgrounds, and to learn about the realities of life in different communities'. He believes the scheme for 16-year-olds would have a similar effect on their development into responsible adults. Youngsters from all backgrounds would take part together and it should be challenging and exciting. 'National Service did bring people together and say, "Look, you're part of something bigger than yourself, part of a country, and you have responsibilities and duties as a citizen". That's what I think we ought to be doing.'

5 The Conservative leader initially intended the national volunteer scheme to be compulsory for 16-year-olds, but modified it to a voluntary one in response to criticism. Opponents argue that the young people most likely to be involved in antisocial behaviour are unlikely to join it. There are already similar activities such as the Duke of Edinburgh Award and Gordon Brown's new volunteer scheme known as 'V'. Young people not interested in joining those are no more likely to be attracted by Cameron's new venture.

6 Labour's David Miliband said: 'Residential opportunities are important for young people, but the problem with David Cameron's proposals is that they are neither costed nor funded. All the evidence is that this would be hugely expensive and he hasn't a clue how he will pay for it.'

7 Cameron admits the cost of the scheme has not yet been calculated, but by discouraging crime and antisocial behaviour it would ultimately save money. He said: 'It's about explaining to young people that we're all in it together. Life's not about me, me, me, it's about us, it's about bringing people together.'

Adapted from a number of sites including BBC Online, the *Independent*, the *Scotsman* and the *Guardian*.

1 Comment on the coherence of the reasoning in paragraph 1.

2 What is implied by David Cameron's comment about the national volunteer scheme that 'we can't afford not to make it work'?

3 Paragraph 3 begins with the words: *Governments have a duty to provide opportunities for young people.* Name this component of argument.

4 Identify the analogy in paragraph 4.

5 Assess the effectiveness of the analogy in paragraph 4.

6 Identify an inconsistency in the criticisms of David Cameron's scheme described in paragraph 5.

7 Consider David Miliband's repudiation of David Cameron's suggestions (paragraph 6). Make two points of assessment of Miliband's comments.

8 Identify two weaknesses in David Cameron's reasoning in paragraph 7.

9 Suggest one point that could be made to support David Cameron's scheme.

10 Suggest one point that could be made to challenge David Cameron's scheme.

Section 2: Evaluating arguments

Flaws in reasoning

As well as false assumptions and disanalogies, which have already been discussed, a number of other **flaws** or weaknesses in reasoning can be identified. These can result from illogical or careless thinking, or through an attempt to persuade by arousing emotion rather than providing sound evidence. Some flaws occur so often that they have been given special names. In the Unit 2 examination you will earn marks for evaluating reasoning (Assessment Objective 2) if you can:

- identify and name flaws
- explain the presence of the flaw in a particular context (how did you recognise this flaw?)
- explain why this type of reasoning is flawed

Errors of muddled thinking

Circular argument

This is also known as **begging the question**. Look at the following example and work out the flaw.

'Why do you believe the theory that the pyramids were built by aliens?'

'Because it says so in Erich von Däniken's book Chariots of the Gods.*'*

'But why do you think the evidence in the book is true?'

'Because the cover of the book says that the theory is "amazingly convincing".'

This argument appears at first to offer useful new information, but the line of reasoning only leads back to the beginning so that the case is not made convincingly. The evidence is not supported by any independent source that can be investigated.

Conflation

This means treating two different concepts as if they were the same.

Vegetarians, vegans and others who worry about ethical consumption are well-meaning but could be damaging their health. Vegetarianism is totally impractical. Not eating any animal product such as eggs, milk and cheese limits the diet far too much, risking calcium deficiency.

In this example, the arguer has criticised vegetarianism but described the diet of a vegan.

Confusions concerning cause and effect

Many arguments rest on the assumption that if two factors are found to occur at the same time or increase at the same rate (correlation), one has caused the other. For example, juvenile crime figures have increased since the 1970s and over the same period a higher proportion of mothers have undertaken paid work. Many people interpret this correlation as suggesting that juvenile crime would be reduced if mothers could be persuaded to stay at home. However, there is no proof that the higher rate of mothers working is responsible for the increase in young people's criminal activities. Many other factors have changed during the same period, such as the increase in divorce, a reduction in the number of unskilled jobs and the weakening of religious belief. Any of these factors could be responsible for the rise of juvenile crime, individually or in combination.

The false assumption that correlation between two factors means that one has caused the other is known as '**correlation = cause confusion**'. An alternative but less specific term is '**false cause**'.

A variation on this is the assumption that one factor has caused the other when it is actually the other way round. A situation could be imagined where more mothers might choose paid work in order to escape from having to spend so much time with their already delinquent children. In such a case, those who attributed the young people's delinquency to their mothers' absence would be **confusing cause and effect**. Assuming causation without clear evidence and **over-simplifying causal relationships** are common errors, particularly in areas such as media reporting and the social sciences.

Post hoc

Post hoc means 'after this'. It refers to the assumption '*what happened after this must have happened because of this'*. It is a variation of the error above, but refers to single incidents rather than a pattern of events. For example, a superstitious student might believe that she did well in a test because she had a 'lucky mascot' with her. Another person might attribute an unfortunate event to having just said that things were going well without saying 'Touch wood'. You might be feeling ill and attribute it to having recently met a friend who had flu, but it may be equally likely that your illness has some other cause.

Confusion of necessary and sufficient conditions

A **necessary** condition is vital in order for something to happen, e.g. police clearance is necessary to obtain a teaching job in Britain. A **sufficient** condition guarantees that the next step must follow; in other words, it is all that is needed. In this example, a combination of academic qualifications, good references and relevant experience in addition to police clearance might be sufficient for a prospective teacher to stand a realistic chance of employment. An optimistic candidate who thought that police clearance alone was enough to get a teaching job would be confusing necessary and sufficient conditions.

Predictions about the future without sufficient evidence

If trends continue is an expression frequently used by the media. It is common to project a particular pattern into the future, often with alarming consequences. This is often done as part of a **moral panic** to support a particular viewpoint, such as the need to address increasing youth disorder by organising a national volunteer scheme. In reality, events often develop following a different pattern.

Restricting the options (false dichotomy)

This type of argument presents listeners or readers with a choice between a limited number of actions, normally two. This is usually done to persuade them to opt for the least undesirable, when in fact there are other more attractive possibilities that the arguer has not presented and perhaps not even thought of. An example is the contention that, as wind power cannot meet all our energy needs, we must develop nuclear power. Unstated alternatives include greater use of solar and wave power and encouraging energy efficiency.

Sweeping generalisation

This is a universal claim that may not be true for all examples, e.g. *people without A-levels will be rejected from universities.* This is not true in the case of those who have alternative qualifications such as the International Baccalaureate. The flaw is also known as **unwarranted** or **hasty generalisation**.

Unrelated conclusion

This involves arguing from one thing to another without cogency, for example the arguer presents fairly persuasive evidence that seems to support a particular conclusion but then moves in a different direction without making a convincing link, so that the final conclusion does not follow. In cases where two concepts are muddled, this could be described as conflation.

Exercise 6a

Read the following passages and name the flaws. In each case, explain how you can recognise the flaw in this particular context.

1 This prospectus says that a Grade 8 qualification in music is required for applicants to the Music Diploma. I've got Grade 8, so I should be able to get on the course.

2 Early in the nineteenth century, men, women and children all worked in factories, mines and mills in horrendous conditions.

3 Students in year 13 opt either to go straight to university or to take a year out, often to see the world. As you haven't made any plans for travelling, you ought to go to university straight away.

4 My experience confirms that four-leaf clovers are lucky. Two days after finding one, I found out I had passed all my GCSEs.

5 As British society has become affluent and increasing numbers of people can afford multiple television sets and computers, so the rate of mental illness has gone up. It is clear that the tendency of parents to sit their children in front of 'electronic babysitters', instead of communicating with them as they used to, is responsible for the mental instability of so many young people.

Exercise 6b

Read the following passages and name the flaws. Then explain in your own words why each flaw you have identified is regarded as poor reasoning.

1 Homosexual acts must be wrong because the Old Testament condemns them and this book is the word of God. Although many people question the existence of God, the Old Testament provides convincing evidence for his existence and influence.

2 There is widespread agreement that international fish stocks are declining and may soon be below replacement level, so fishing limits must be set and adhered to. We should therefore support Greenpeace's attempts to disrupt Japanese plans to kill up to 1,000 whales in the Southern Ocean.

3 The divorce rate in England and Wales has fallen each year since 2004. Clearly, people are becoming happier in their marriages and we can look forward to a situation in a few years' time when hardly any couples will seek to end their marriages.

4 The rail fare to Edinburgh is excessively expensive so, much as I would prefer to use public transport to safeguard the environment, I have no choice but to drive there.

5 Alcoholism is a major problem among Australia's aboriginal population, many of whom are unemployed. Clearly, over-indulgence in alcohol weakens the drive to seek work. It will also reduce the employability of potential workers because of their unreliability and, eventually, their deteriorating health.

Arousing emotion instead of reasoning logically

Some erroneous patterns of reasoning mislead people by arousing emotion, which tends to distract attention from the argument's lack of logic. Four such common flaws are described below.

Ad hominem ('to the man')

This technique involves criticising some feature of an opponent so that people dismiss his or her argument without giving it serious consideration. For example, a Conservative MP might, instead of discussing a suggestion made by a Labour MP about how to reduce global warming, remind the House of Commons of the Labour MP's alleged involvement in a 'sleaze' incident the previous year. As participation in dishonest practice, even if true, has no relevance to a person's expertise about global warming, this is a clear case of trying to discredit an opponent by raising feelings against him or her rather than having to think of convincing counter-arguments.

Straw man or straw person

This is a similar technique to *ad hominem*. The arguer finds some minor weakness in the opponent's suggestion, such as a small exceptional group for whom the proposed scheme would not be beneficial. This trivial negative aspect is then exaggerated, taking the focus away from the many strengths of the opponent's position. The whole argument or plan can then be 'blown away', as easily as if it were a man built flimsily out of straw. Here is an example.

It would be a foolish idea to provide free daily milk to primary school children. Some children have dairy allergies and could be made extremely ill as a result. Their allergic condition might not be diagnosed for a long period, with teachers and parents assuming their symptoms were the result of some disease. By providing free milk, schools would therefore be responsible for disrupting the health and ability to perform at their best of the pupils in their charge.

Slippery slope or the thin end of the wedge

This is a chain of arguments that starts with a moderate claim and predicts a series of events leading to an alarming outcome. It works by arousing so much fear that the reader or listener fails to question whether each event will inevitably lead to the next. An example is as follows.

If we permit our pupils under the age of 16 to wear discreet make-up, some of them will take advantage and wear extreme make-up. This will draw the attention of unsavoury characters in the streets and the girls will risk sexual harassment and rape. They may be approached by pimps and lured into prostitution, and their promising lives will be ruined by disease, violence and premature death. We must therefore deny the School Council's request for pupils to be allowed to wear discreet make-up.

Tu quoque ('you too')

This involves deflecting what might be sound criticism by accusing the critic of being guilty of the same or a similar fault. A variation is to point out that other people have committed the act so it cannot be wrong. This is illogical because 'two wrongs don't make a right'.

It was ridiculous of the policewoman to fine me for speeding. Everyone does it, even members of the royal family.

Appeals

Appeals are **rhetorical devices** because they act as a substitute for rational argument, and as such they may be regarded as weaknesses in reasoning.

Appeals to emotion may arouse fear, for example British National Party election material paints an extreme picture of Britain being overrun with immigrants. Some extremist political material arouses hatred, whereas advertisements for beauty products appeal to people's desire to be attractive. Charity appeals usually evoke our pity through loaded language, although they may also provide good reasons and evidence for why we should donate.

Appeal to tradition involves taking the view that something should be done in the same way it has always been done, because the old ways have been successful. Unless there is clear evidence that the approach adopted in the past was the best and will continue to be so in today's changed conditions, this is simply an appeal to nostalgia.

Sometimes the appeal to tradition is known as an **appeal to history** instead. However, there is another type of appeal to history, involving predicting future events on the basis of what has happened in the past. Although historians claim that studying their subject helps to warn us against making the same mistakes twice, exactly the same situation never recurs. It might have been unwise of Chamberlain to try to placate Hitler instead of opposing him from the start, but that does not necessarily mean it would be wise for subsequent national leaders to take a militant approach to every dictator.

In an **appeal to authority**, an arguer may claim that some authority figure supports the conclusion being proposed instead of providing another type of evidence. While this might add to credibility if the person is an expert in the relevant field, you would need to be sure that this was the case. Even so, such an appeal might provide inadequate support if other experts held a different view or if the authority figure had a bias or vested interest. If the arguer failed to name the authority figure and simply referred to 'experts', there would be no way to validate the legitimacy of the expertise.

Appeal to popularity acknowledges that we may be swayed to believe a claim if told that it is a majority belief, but this is not sufficient to prove its truth. Members of the general public rely for most of their information on experts or the media, and both of these can be misled. History is full of widely held erroneous beliefs, such as the long-accepted view that the Sun orbited the Earth.

Exercise 7

In the passages below, identify the flaws and appeals by name, quoting the relevant phrases and making it clear why there is a problem with the author's reasoning.

Passage A

Cherie Blair's ideas on alternatives to prison for pregnant women are not worthy of consideration. In 2002, she was accused of buying a flat for her son with help from a convicted fraudster, Peter Foster.

Passage B

We are letting too many juveniles run our lives. This explains why Blair got us into Iraq. There was nobody old and wise enough in cabinet to convince him otherwise. These little politicians we are elevating because they look good before the camera will always let us down because they are still too young and too idealistic and most of them are spoiled little rich brats riding high on family wealth to high offices.

Letter to *Guardian Online*, 26 January 2008

http://politics.guardian.co.uk/columnist/story/0,,2247332,00.html

Passage C

The internet is vastly overrated. My attempts at using it for research have been frequently interrupted by irritating and sometimes offensive advertising pop-ups. People should be discouraged from wasting their money and time on computers.

Passage D

Scientology can unite cultures and bring world peace. The Hollywood star Tom Cruise said this in a video about the religious movement, so we ought to join and give it our full support.

Passage E

The recent murders of and by young people, especially in London, show that our streets are becoming increasingly dangerous. Soon it may be too hazardous to go out almost anywhere, and more and more people will opt to work from home to avoid the risks. Restaurants and cinemas will close down as no one ventures into the streets and young people will be unable to meet others. Finding partners will be virtually impossible, so in a short time the human race will dramatically shrink in number.

Passage F

Tony Blair took Britain to war with Iraq quite unnecessarily as there were no weapons of mass destruction, despite his fears. Next time we hear that a hostile nation is amassing such weapons, we shall know that the best policy is to ignore the rumours and take no action.

Passage G

The teacher told me to improve my handwriting before the examination but I'm not going to bother. When she writes comments on my essays, I often can't read them so who's she to talk?

Assessing strengths and weaknesses

Unit 1 introduced you to the assessment of evidence. In Unit 2, you are required to assess whether evidence is sufficiently relevant and adequate to support a conclusion. It is important to consider whether evidence from surveys or similar research is based upon a **large and representative sample** and whether it is **recent** and **pertinent** (closely relevant) to the situation being discussed.

Think carefully about any statistics being presented. For example, displays of central tendency such as **median** (calculated by sorting the data set from the lowest to highest values and taking the data point in the middle of the sequence) or a **mean** (commonly referred to as an 'average', and the sum of the values divided by the total number of items in the set) do not convey the full range of scores. This may mask extremes which, if presented, might alter the overall impression of the data.

It is crucial to understand the difference between **percentages**, **rates** (e.g. the number per thousand or per million), **proportions** and **raw numbers** — confusion between these may make data misleading. On the other hand, an argument will be strengthened if it is supported by relevant and convincing research and statistics.

Sometimes you may use some of the **credibility criteria** covered in Unit 1 to assess evidence and arguments. Arguments may be strong because they are presented by named **experts** who appear to be **neutral** and have first-hand knowledge of a particular situation (**ability to perceive**). Evidence may be weak because it is based on **hearsay** and those making the claim have **vested interests**.

Weaknesses in arguments include all the **flaws** named in the previous section and **emotional appeals**. In addition, you may need to identify and assess analogies to decide whether they strengthen or fail to support arguments. Consider the extent to which **hypothetical arguments** add legitimacy to a claim and how fully **general principles** apply. Assess whether **examples** given are apt or poor, and whether **assumptions** made are reasonable. You may need to judge whether the **links** made between two points are logical and whether the argument as a whole is **coherent**.

You may also be asked to suggest other conclusions that could reasonably be drawn from the evidence provided or to identify explanations given and offer well-founded alternatives.

Remember that if you are asked to assess or criticise part of an argument, this invites you to identify strengths as well as weaknesses.

Exercise 8

Read the passages that follow and answer the questions in the spaces provided.

Teachers angry at proposed wage cut

Gordon Brown will face a test of his plans to hold down public sector pay after the announcement of a 3-year pay deal for teachers in England and Wales this week.

The deal would give teachers a pay rise of 2.45% this year, and 2.3% for the following 2 years. Inflation, as measured by the retail price index, is currently at 4%. The deal would effectively give teachers 3 years of pay cuts.

Responding to the deal, National Union of Teachers' general secretary Steve Sinnott said, 'Teachers will be worse off'.

The NUT has promised a 'robust' response to the offer.

Adapted from *Socialist Worker* online, 19 January 2008
www.socialistworker.co.uk/art.php?id=13941

1 Examine the statistics in the passage and assess the appropriateness of the headline.

Skills shortage addressed

According to the government-commissioned Leitch Review of Skills, basic skills have improved in the UK. But, despite this, 1 in 6 adults does not have the literacy skills expected of an 11-year-old and half do not have these levels of functional numeracy.

The national skills shortage may soon be solved as employees will be able to gain GCSE-equivalent qualifications in numeracy or literacy at work. Branches of McDonald's are to become exam centres as the fast-food chain sets up a web-based scheme enabling their 67,000 staff to improve their numeracy and literacy with the support of an online tutor. McDonald's expects up to 1,000 employees to gain nationally recognised Level 1 and 2 qualifications in accredited exam-centre restaurants. Level 1 is the equivalent to an NVQ Level 1 or GCSE grade D–G, while Level 2 is equal to an NVQ Level 2 or GCSE grade A–C. The tests are from exam board OCR.

Adapted from BBC News Online, 19 September 2006
http://news.bbc.co.uk/1/hi/education/5356176.stm

2 Identify the main conclusion of the passage.

3 Suggest several questions you might want to ask about research conducted by the Leitch Review of Skills before accepting its findings.

4 To what extent is the evidence provided in the second paragraph strong enough to support the conclusion? Make at least three points of assessment.

Section 3: Multiple-choice questions

Section A of the Unit 2 examination consists of multiple-choice questions based on stimulus material in the form of short passages, charts and diagrams. Some of the passages may generate more than one set of questions. This section tests your ability to analyse the structure of arguments (AO1) and to assess arguments and evidence (AO2). It is recommended that you consult past papers on the OCR website for examples of a wide range of specimen questions.

It is a good idea to look at the question first before studying the passage, in order to focus your mind straight away on what you are looking for. Then read the passage and decide what you think the answer is before examining the options. In this way, you are less likely to be distracted by options that are incorrect.

The approach of using a process of elimination is only recommended if you have little idea about what the answer could be. There is often one answer that is the opposite of the correct one, one that has little relevance and two that are similar, one of which is the 'best statement' of the answer. Identify the exact difference in meaning between the options to select the correct one. If you really cannot decide, choose one of the better options randomly and move on, as you need to spend not much more than a minute per question in order to leave adequate time for the completion of Sections B and C.

Exercise 9

Read the passages below and choose one option in answer to each question, ticking the appropriate boxes.

The laws on stop and search need to be changed so that police can more easily deter people from carrying weapons in the street. At present, when police simply ask a person to account for his or her movements they have to fill in a foot-long form that takes about 7 minutes. Instead, they should be able to speak the details into a voice recorder that relays the information to their police station.

Likewise, the restrictions governing searches need to be reduced. Currently, unless there are definite grounds for suspicion, searches can only be conducted in certain areas with the agreement of a police inspector. It would be much more effective if all police officers were allowed to conduct random searches, as innocent people would have nothing to lose.

Although some people fear that ethnic minorities may be disproportionately targeted in stop and searches, British Asian and black youths are being stabbed and shot because little is done to stop their assailants carrying weapons.

1 Which of the following is the main conclusion of the above argument?

- A The laws on stop and search need to be changed.
- B Police should be able to speak the details of stop and searches into a voice recorder that relays the information to their police station.
- C The restrictions governing searches need to be reduced.
- D Little is done to stop the assailants of British Asian and black youths carrying weapons.

2 Which of the following components of argument is the phrase 'some people fear that ethnic minorities may be disproportionately targeted in stop and searches'?

- **A** explanation
- **B** reason
- **C** counter-claim
- **D** example

3 Which one of the following, if true, would **not** weaken the argument?

- **A** There is evidence from the Scarman Report that innocent people develop anti-police attitudes if randomly stopped and searched.
- **B** White youths are just as likely to be victims of knife and gun attacks as black and Asian youths.
- **C** Random searches are an inefficient use of police time as they result in relatively few convictions.
- **D** Speaking details about each stop into a voice recorder would take almost as much police time as filling in a form.

David Cameron has suggested that a maternity nurse should assist every new mother in her home for up to 6 hours a day in the first week after the baby's birth. The nurse's tasks would include showing new mothers how to breastfeed and bathe their baby, looking after older children and making sure healthy meals are provided, monitoring visitors to ensure that the mother's rest times are not interrupted and keeping a diary with details of the mother and baby's progress for use by doctors and midwives.

This suggestion is a clear example of the 'nanny state'. Employing officials to interfere with a family's diet and keep away visitors is intruding far too much in personal lives. Who knows what private details may be passed on to other busybody officials through the nurse's diary and, with the current government record for losing personal data, how many families might be blackmailed in the future or have their identities stolen?

4 Which of the following is **not** a feature of the second paragraph of the passage above?

- **A** slippery slope
- **B** appeal to fear
- **C** hypothetical reasoning
- **D** *ad hominem*

5 Which of the following is the most appropriate conclusion to be drawn from the above passage?

- **A** If maternity nurses help new mothers in their homes, their role should be restricted to matters of childcare.
- **B** New mothers can manage in the early days after childbirth without help.
- **C** The government should not employ staff to go into people's homes.
- **D** The maternity nurse scheme is a government plot to find out about people's private lives.

6 Which of the following is the closest in meaning to '*nanny state*' as used in the passage?

- **A** a situation in which the government employs professionals to look after children
- **B** a nation in which the government intervenes too much to protect the welfare of its citizens
- **C** a government that tries to collect information about its citizens' private lives
- **D** a situation in which baby care is prioritised over the needs of adults

Section 4: Developing reasoned arguments

Section C of Unit 2 requires you to demonstrate the ability to write your own logically structured and convincing arguments on a given topic.

To obtain top-level marks, it is important to think carefully about exactly what conclusion you are drawing. You may be asked to support or challenge the conclusion of the passage provided. Make sure you identify the conclusion carefully and that all your reasons support or challenge it precisely. For example, if the conclusion is that no more roads should be built, you should not stray into arguments suggesting that cars should be banned.

Remember that writing an argument of your own means that you must not repeat any of the arguments or evidence used in the passage, although occasionally, if challenging the conclusion, you may be able to interpret some of the evidence differently.

Look carefully at the list of components required in the argument, e.g. counter-argument, reasons, evidence, examples and intermediate conclusions. Structure your argument instead of writing freely on the subject as you might do in a subject such as English.

If you have enough time and ideas, include more components than the minimum requirement. If the question asks for 'an intermediate conclusion supported by two or more reasons and evidence or examples', consider including two intermediate conclusions, each supported by a couple of reasons and both evidence and examples.

As there are a considerable number of marks available for writing an argument, examiners expect high quality of content as well as a logical structure. Ensure that your argument is convincing, requiring only a few reasonable assumptions. The intermediate conclusions must be fully supported by the reasons and evidence, and all the components must lead logically to the final conclusion.

Exercise 10

Before you attempt to write your own argument, identify the component parts of the following argument, which is about as ambitious in structure as you can expect to encounter at AS. Identify the elements by annotating them with symbols such as R1, IC1 (first intermediate conclusion), C, CA (counter-argument) and RCA (response to the counter-argument).

Many people are attracted to Rome and Florence because of their historical sights ______, but both have busy roads and are hot in summer ______. Venice has equally attractive sights ______, such as St Mark's Cathedral and the Doge's palace ______, and there is no motor traffic ______. People travel around the island by gondola, canal boat or on foot ______, so it is a suitable choice for the history lover who dislikes traffic ______.

Being in the north of Italy, Venice is relatively cool ______. If the day is uncomfortably warm, it is refreshing and convenient to travel out to the islands ______. A boat trip to the islands of Burano and Torcello can easily be achieved in one day at moderate cost ______.

Venice is therefore a better choice than Rome or Florence for those who shun the heat ______. It has the added advantage of a cuisine of fresh, local seafood ______, with delights such as squid, octopus and clams ______.

Anyone who enjoys Italian historical sights and seeks a relatively cool, traffic-free holiday and interesting cuisine should seriously contemplate a visit to Venice ______.

Exercise 11

After checking that your analysis of the structure of the argument in Exercise 10 was correct, try writing your own argument by using its basic structure as a model. Your argument could be in favour of your own choice of holiday resort, with a brief counter-argument about the merits of another destination, which you then dismiss. Alternatively, argue in favour of some activity you enjoy, adopting a similar structure. Annotate your work with symbols, so that your teacher or a fellow student can identify and check the intended structure.

Exercise 12

Read the short passage on p. 35 and then write your own argument, challenging its main conclusion.

Marks will be given for a well-structured, convincing and developed argument that contains at least three reasons, intermediate conclusions and an overall conclusion. Your argument should also contain examples and/or evidence and a counter-argument that you dismiss.

If you wish to seek information on this topic to provide you with evidence for your argument, the following websites will be helpful:

Citizenship Foundation site, controversial topics section:
www.citizenshipfoundation.org.uk/main/page.php?105#note_1

League Against Cruel Sports
www.league.org.uk/content.asp?CategoryID=1709

It was quite wrong to ban fox-hunting with hounds.

Foxes are pests, as can easily be illustrated if you visit a chicken farm and see the devastation after a fox has slipped into the henhouse. Hunting controls the fox population in a manner that usually brings a less lingering death than trapping the animals, so it is a practice of which many farmers approve.

Banning fox-hunting will result in the loss of many jobs. At least 6,000 people are directly employed, such as those who breed and look after hounds, and many others will be affected by loss of trade if hunters no longer assemble in country venues such as hotels and pubs to participate in hunting.

Fox-hunting is a traditional sport. Britain is changing so rapidly that we should think twice about banning a sport that has long been part of our culture.

Section 5: Specimen examination paper

The time allowed for this paper is 1 hour 30 minutes, and the total number of marks is 75. The marks for each question are given in brackets, except for Section A, where each answer is worth 1 mark.

Read the documents carefully before starting to answer the questions.

Section A: Multiple-choice questions

1

Although the production of palm oil in countries such as Indonesia boosts industrial and rural development, in climate terms, razing rainforests to grow palm oil for biofuels is madness. Clearing a hectare of tropical forest releases between 500 and 900 tonnes of carbon dioxide. Since turning a hectare's worth of palm oil into biodiesel saves approximately 6 tonnes of fossil fuel carbon dioxide emissions a year, it will take 80 to 150 years of production to offset the one-off emissions from trashing the forest. If the forest is growing on a peat bog, the carbon dioxide losses are far greater and continue far longer, as peat releases the gas as it dries and decomposes.

Which of the following is the **main conclusion** of the above argument?

- **A** The production of palm oil in countries such as Indonesia boosts industrial and rural development.
- **B** In climate terms, razing rainforests to grow palm oil for biofuels is madness.
- **C** It will take 80 to 150 years of production to offset the one-off emissions from trashing the forest.
- **D** Carbon dioxide losses are far greater from the felling of tropical forests where they are growing in peat bogs.

Questions 2, 3, 4 and 5 refer to the following passage.

Since the murder of Garry Newlove by three youths, one of whom had been released on bail while awaiting trial for another violent offence, members of the public have been questioning whether bail is permitted too often. However, our prisons are too overcrowded to accommodate all the people awaiting trial, so it would need a large increase in taxes to build new prisons, employ extra guards and pay for the upkeep of all those accused of crimes. It is better to allow people who may have to wait a year or more for their trial to work and support their families.

Someone accused of a crime on slight evidence, such as a teacher accused of assault by a possibly malicious pupil, might be traumatised by sharing a prison cell with hardened criminals. Everyone should be presumed innocent until proven guilty, so it would be absurd to remand a person in custody who is alleged to have committed a fairly minor crime and has no previous convictions, particularly if the evidence against him or her is weak. In such cases, granting bail is preferable to imprisoning those awaiting trial.

2 Which of the following is the best description of how the phrase 'Everyone should be presumed innocent until proven guilty' is used in the passage?

- **A** conclusion
- **B** intermediate conclusion
- **C** principle

D counter-claim

3 Which of the following is **not** a reasonable criticism of the argument?

A There is a mismatch between the beginning of the argument, about whether bail is permitted too often, for example for violent offenders, and the conclusion, which justifies bail for those accused of fairly minor crimes.

B The argument that prisons are too overcrowded to accommodate 'all the people awaiting trial' is not strictly relevant to the issue of whether bail is permitted 'too often'.

C There is an assumption that those accused of crimes are largely employed heads of families, whereas many could be unemployed and tempted into further crime.

D There is an unjustified assumption that teachers accused of assault by their pupils are always innocent.

4 Which of the following statements about the components of the passage is **not** true?

A The reference to the Garry Newlove murder is scene-setting.

B The reference to the teacher is a counter-example to the argument.

C 'It is better to allow people who may have to wait a year or more for their trial to work and support their families' is an intermediate conclusion.

D The reference to the teacher includes an appeal to pity.

5 Which of the following, if true, would **most weaken** the conclusion of the above argument?

A The average length of prison sentence awarded to those found guilty of fairly minor crimes is likely to be less than the average amount of time accused people spend awaiting trial.

B People found guilty of fairly minor offences who have no previous convictions are more likely to be punished by fines or community service than by custodial sentences.

C Magistrates and juries are instructed not to bring a guilty verdict in cases of reasonable doubt.

D All offenders begin their criminal careers with no previous convictions. It is not evidence of innocence.

6

The number of death certificates in England and Wales mentioning *Clostridium difficile* (*C. diff*) infection has increased every year since 1999. *C. diff* is a spore-forming bacterium that is present as one of the 'normal' bacteria in the gut of up to 3% of healthy adults. Patients who have been treated with broad-spectrum antibiotics are at greatest risk of *C. diff*-associated disease. In addition, risks of contracting *C. diff* are raised for patients who are elderly, have a serious underlying illness that compromises their immune system, have a prolonged stay in healthcare settings, or have recently had gastrointestinal surgery.

Patients are also at risk of developing *C. diff* disease when there are outbreaks in hospitals. Latest mortality rates for deaths involving *C. diff* in the 85 and over age group were 1,580 and 1,812 deaths per million population for males and females respectively. In the under-45 age group, there were 0.2 deaths per million population for both males and females.

Which of the following conclusions is least compatible with the information in the passage?

A The higher mortality rate from *C. diff* for elderly people may be partly because they are more likely than the young to have serious underlying illnesses.

B The higher mortality rate from *C. diff* for elderly people may be partly because they are more likely to be in hospital for prolonged periods.

C Under-45s who have been treated with broad-spectrum antibiotics have little risk of contracting *C. diff.*

D Patients of all ages are vulnerable to *C. diff* disease if there is an outbreak in their hospital.

7

Living arrangements 2004–05 in the UK

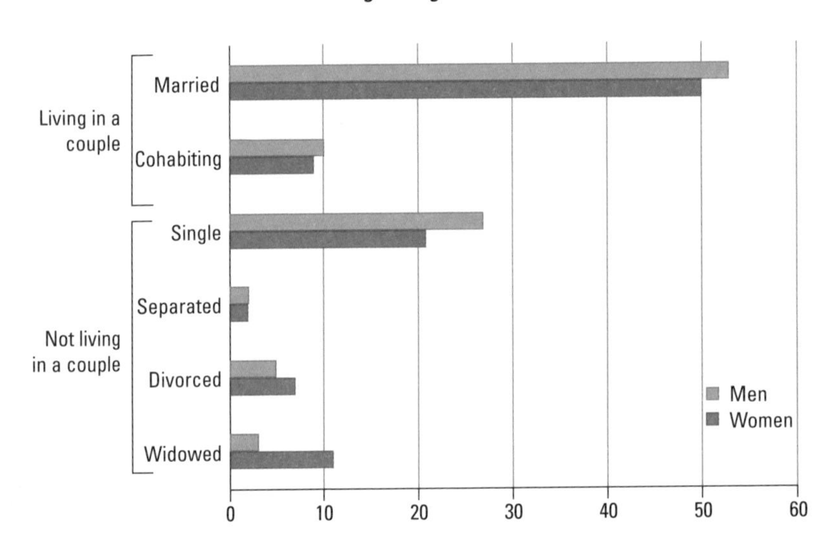

Data related to cohabitation are for people aged 16 to 59. All other data relate to people aged 16 and over. Figures shown are percentages.

Adapted from National Statistics Online: Families
www.statistics.gov.uk/focuson/families/

Which of the following is **not** a possible explanation of the data on the graph?

A The different length of line for males and females who are married could be explained by the fact that some of the men may be migrants who have left their wives abroad.

B The different length of line for males and females who are married could be explained by the fact that the figures relate to percentages and not numbers.

C The different length of line for males and females who are cohabiting (living together unmarried) could be explained by the possibility that women may be less willing to admit to this than men.

D The different length of line for males and females who are divorced could be explained if men were more inclined to remarry after divorce and then divorce again, whereas women were more reluctant to marry again after one divorce.

Questions 8, 9 and 10 refer to the following passage.

It is estimated that at least 55% of British Pakistanis are married to first cousins, but parents should be encouraged to look outside the family for partners for their young people. Marrying a close family member carries a risk for children. Communities that practise cousin marriage experience higher levels of some rare but serious illnesses known as recessive genetic disorders.

Many British Pakistanis celebrate cousin marriage because it is believed to generate more stable and close relationships. On family occasions, the relatives of both partners already know each other and share the same background.

However, British Pakistanis are much more likely to have children with genetic disorders than the general population. They account for just over 3% of all births but have just under a third of all British children with such illnesses.

Recessive genetic disorders are caused by variant genes. There are hundreds of different recessive genetic disorders, many associated with severe disability and sometimes early death, and each caused by a different variant gene. We all have two copies of every gene. As a result, a child that inherits one variant gene will not fall ill. If, however, a child inherits a copy of the same variant gene from each of its parents, it will develop one of these illnesses. The variant genes that cause genetic illness tend to be rare. In the general population, the likelihood of a couple having the same variant gene is a hundred to one. In cousin marriages, if one partner has a variant gene the risk that the other has it too is far higher, more like one in eight.

Ann Cryer MP, whose Keighley constituency has a large Pakistani population, claims that the community is in denial about the problem and needs to discuss it. 'As we address the problem of smoking, drinking or obesity, we say it's a public health issue,' she says. 'I think the same should be applied to this problem in the Asian community.'

Adapted from BBC News Online, 16 November 2005 http://news.bbc.co.uk/1/hi/programmes/newsnight/4442010.stm

8 Which of the following is the best statement of the main conclusion of the argument?

- **A** Parents should be encouraged to look outside the family for partners for their young people.
- **B** Marrying a close family member carries a risk for children.
- **C** British Pakistanis are much more likely to have children with genetic disorders than the general population.
- **D** The problem of first-cousin marriage is a public health issue.

9 Which of the following comments about components of the above argument is **not** true?

- **A** The second paragraph is a counter-argument.
- **B** The reference to Ann Cryer MP is an appeal to authority.
- **C** In the final paragraph, Ann Cryer makes use of an analogy.
- **D** The issue of first-cousin marriages leading to child illnesses is a slippery-slope argument.

10 Which one of the following can definitely be established from the above argument?

- **A** Marriages between first cousins are happier than other marriages.
- **B** Couples who do not marry relatives will not have children with recessive genetic disorders.
- **C** The higher than average incidence of rare diseases in the children of married cousins is likely to stem from the greater chance of both partners carrying the same variant genes.
- **D** First-cousin marriages constitute greater health risks for British Pakistanis than smoking, drinking and obesity.

11

Iain Duncan-Smith, the former Conservative leader who has since been replaced by the more charismatic David Cameron, has been investigating the causes of 'Breakdown Britain'. His findings suggest one of the reasons behind the recent spate of horrific crimes by the young is family breakdown.

In the 1950s, when most mothers stayed at home with their children, there was far less recorded crime by children and teenagers than there is now. Since the feminist movement encouraged married women to aspire to careers, juvenile delinquency figures have increased dramatically. Now 55% of working-age women with children under 5 are in the labour force, while 73% of women whose youngest child is aged between 5 and 10 do paid work. Of women whose youngest child is aged 11 to 15, the peak age for delinquency, 80% work outside the home. It is clear that, if we want to reverse the rise in child crime, we must encourage mothers to resist the lure of paid work and stay at home.

Which of the following flaws in reasoning is **not** a feature of the above argument?

- **A** correlation = cause confusion
- **B** conflation between family breakdown and mothers working
- **C** *ad hominem*
- **D** no account taken of the fact that juvenile offences were often not recorded in the 1950s; police tended to deal with such matters informally

12

The government's education agenda is influenced by a culture of change. The latest innovation is that secondary school students should have time allocated each week for activities such as visiting galleries, concerts, theatres and museums, playing instruments and creative writing.

A few years ago, multiculturalism was the vogue, and school curricula were packed with topics relating to different cultures, such as studying black writers and finding out about Diwali, the Hindu festival of lights. Tony Blair encouraged the foundation of new faith schools, pleasing some ethnic minorities, but since the London bombings both government and opposition have been keener to foster a sense of shared British culture and the expansion of faith schools has been abandoned. Now this latest initiative is turning its back on the rigid national curriculum established in 1988, funding schools to provide 5 hours a week of culture for every secondary school student.

Which of the following is the most accurate reflection of how the word 'culture' is used in the final sentence of the passage?

- **A** the language and religious customs of a particular ethnic group
- **B** a predominant attitude or way of thinking
- **C** arts such as music, drama, literature and painting
- **D** identifying with a particular nation, a sense of belonging

13

Lord Dearing's suggestion that British schools should consider switching from teaching European languages to non-European ones is ill-advised. Students will find the unfamiliar symbols of Mandarin so daunting that many will become frustrated. Teenagers are already emotionally vulnerable, so that frustration will lead to depression. Schools will soon have to cope with the traumatising effects of frequent student suicides.

Which of the following is **not** a flaw in the reasoning of the passage?

- **A** an appeal to tradition
- **B** a slippery slope or thin end of the wedge
- **C** a straw person or straw man
- **D** an assumption that the non-European languages scheme is not intended for primary schools

14

Members of the public are unjustifiably alarmed by the Archbishop of Canterbury's observation that adopting aspects of Sharia law in Britain may be unavoidable. Sharia law courts would not deal with criminal law but with civil law. Civil courts make judgements over matters members of the public want settled, such as disputes between neighbours over fences and overhanging trees, and they deal with marital law such as custody of children after divorce. Therefore, Muslims could, if they wish, choose between having disputes settled in a Sharia court or having to await the deliberations of a state-run civil court. Sharia courts would not have the task of trying people accused of serious crimes by the police and imposing harsh punishments.

Which of the following comments about the passage is **untrue**?

- **A** It implies that Sharia courts dealing with marital law is not a cause for concern.
- **B** It assumes that the public mistakenly thought Sharia courts would try to punish people accused of serious crimes.
- **C** It suggests that adopting Sharia law in Britain should be welcomed.
- **D** It implies that Sharia courts are likely to deal with cases more swiftly than state-run civil courts.

15

The Israeli authorities have just renewed the identity card of the woman thought to be the world's oldest person. Mariam Amash claims to be 120, though records kept in the region in the 1880s were sometimes slightly inaccurate, so she could be a couple of years younger or even older. She has certainly beaten the record of Edna Parker of Indiana, who is a mere 114 years old. Mariam Amash, of Bedouin descent, walks every day and makes sure she drinks a daily glass of olive oil. Her health advice to younger generations is that they drink too much Arak, an Arabic alcoholic drink. We can clearly learn from her experience. Drink olive oil and walk regularly to live to a ripe old age or prepare for an early death if you binge drink and rely on your car.

Which of the following is **not** a flaw in the reasoning of the passage?

- **A** There is a sweeping generalisation based upon only one case.
- **B** There is a restricted options flaw in the final sentence.
- **C** There is an assumption of cause and effect that may be unjustified.
- **D** Mariam Amash may be younger than she claims, invalidating the argument.

Section A total: 15 marks

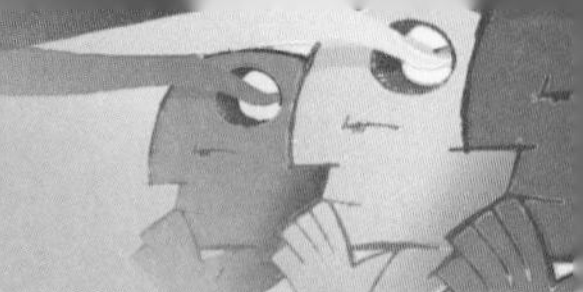

Section B: Analysing and evaluating argument

Read the passage about independent schools and answer all the questions that follow in the spaces provided.

Do independent schools increase the attainment gap?

1 Britain's independent school system is of world-class standard, so we must actively oppose any government attempts to abolish it. Many of today's most successful professionals and business leaders attended fee-charging schools such as Eton, Rugby and Harrow, which were established to train young men to take up important positions in society. It is said that the Battle of Waterloo was won on the playing fields of Eton. Scholars were taught qualities that helped them defend their country, such as physical toughness and willingness to make personal sacrifices to benefit the group. Richard Branson, founder of the Virgin group that owns around 200 music, travel and leisure companies in over 30 countries, was educated at Stowe, an independent school founded in 1923, demonstrating the success of the independent system.

2 As well as encouraging the life skills that bring success, especially for boarders who spend more time absorbing the schools' values, independent schools are renowned for their academic success. They are high up in the GCSE and A-level results league tables and many of their students earn university places.

3 We should support independent schools because of the variety they offer. Some are founded for specific purposes, to promote particular skills, religions or philosophies, such as choir schools, drama schools and faith schools. Former Education Secretary Ruth Kelly recently had to defend her decision to send her child, who has substantial learning difficulties, to an independent school with a large special needs department. Labour MP Ian Gibson opposed her decision, saying she should set an example by supporting her local state school. However, Gibson has recently been preoccupied with the hopeless task of opposing the Japanese government's plans to hunt humpback whales, so his comments on education are unlikely to be well-informed. If independent schools were abolished, all students would be subjected to the same education in the state system, instead of enjoying the present variety of approach. We would end up with a generation of clones, young people all thinking the same, as in the nightmare novel *Brave New World*.

4 Although some people think independent schools are elitist, as last year average day fees topped £8,000 while boarding fees exceeded £20,000, poorer young people benefit from them just as much as their own students. The Charity Commission has said they must now operate for 'public benefit', which means they should consider offering some subsidised or free places or allowing local state schools to use some of their facilities such as playing fields, gyms, computer suites and drama studios.

5 Independent schools are part of British tradition. Housed in ancestral homes in beautiful grounds, they date back to medieval times. Like wine and cheese, they will improve with maturity if left undisturbed.

16 Identify the main conclusion of the argument presented in the passage. (2 marks)

17 Identify the counter-argument. (2 marks)

18 In paragraph 1, Richard Branson's success is quoted as demonstration of the success of the independent system. With reference to material in this paragraph, make two points of criticism of this link. (4 marks)

19 Identify and explain how some of the information in paragraph 3 weakens the claims made in paragraph 2. (2 marks)

20 Paragraph 3 suggests the views of MP Ian Gibson are ill-informed. Name this type of flaw and explain why this way of reasoning is flawed. (3 marks)

21 The reasoning in paragraph 3 uses a slippery slope. With reference to the passage, explain why this way of reasoning is flawed. (3 marks)

22 Evaluate the evidence in the passage supporting the view that independent schools benefit poorer children just as much as their own fee-paying students. (4 marks)

23 Name and describe the flaw in the implication in the final paragraph that independent schools should be preserved because they 'date back to medieval times'. (3 marks)

24 The reasoning in the final paragraph uses an analogy. What is being compared in this analogy? (2 marks)

25 How well does this analogy support the author's suggestion that independent schools should be left undisturbed? (3 marks)

26 Identify a contradiction between material in the first and final paragraphs. (2 marks)

Section B total: 30 marks

Section C: Developing your own arguments

27 In paragraph 1 of the passage on p. 42, the author suggests that many people who attend fee-charging schools are successful because of the personal qualities the schools encourage. Suggest two other reasons why these young people may be particularly successful in business and the professions. (4 marks)

28 Paragraph 2 states that independent schools rank high in GCSE and A-level results league tables. Suggest one reason why these league tables may not be a reliable guide to the quality of a school's teaching. (2 marks)

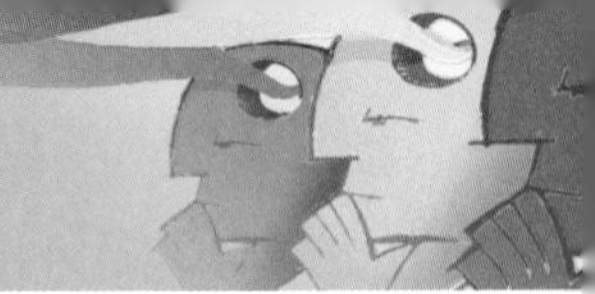

29 Many independent schools take boarders as well as or instead of day pupils, and a small number of state schools take boarders. Consider the advantages and disadvantages of attending a boarding school and construct an argument **either supporting or challenging** the view that 'Parents should strongly consider sending their children to boarding school'. Head your argument to make your choice clear.

Marks will be given for a well-structured argument that contains a counter-argument or counter-claim that is then challenged, at least three reasons, intermediate conclusions and an overall conclusion. Your argument should also contain examples and/or evidence. Ensure that your reasoning is convincing and requires only a few reasonable assumptions. (12 marks)

30 Construct an argument of your own that **challenges** the main conclusion of the passage about independent schools.

Marks will be given for a well-structured and developed argument that contains at least three reasons (one of which should be a principle), intermediate conclusions and an overall conclusion. Your argument should also contain examples and/or evidence.

You may use information and ideas from the original passage, but only to form new arguments. No credit will be given for simply repeating this material. Ensure that your arguments are convincing and require only a few reasonable assumptions. (12 marks)

Section C total: 30 marks